Farmir
in Lincolr

on old picture postcaras

Eric Croft

ISBN 0 946245 99 1

EVERY MACHINE GUARANTEED.

IMPROVED 1905 HORNSBY BINDER.

1. An advert for farm machinery featuring a two horse-drawn binder manufactured by R. Hornsby & Sons Ltd. of Grantham. It was used for cutting and binding the corn into sheaves. The postcard was used in August 1905.

Printed by
Adlard Print and Typesetting Services,
Ruddington, Notts.

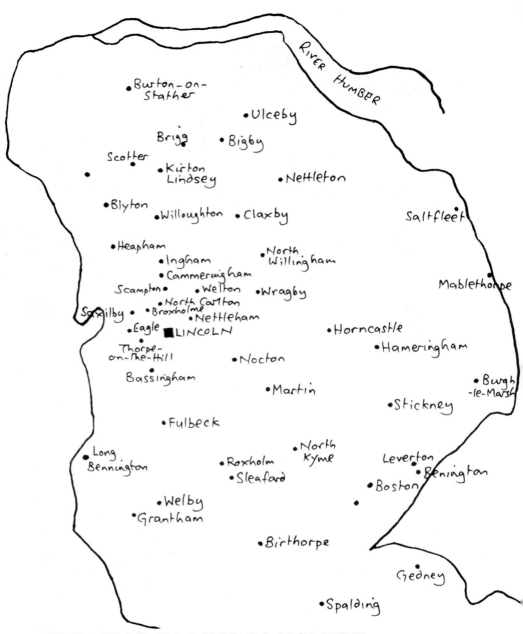

FARMING IN LINCOLNSHIRE

Locations featured in the book

2. Burton-on-Stather. A successful day's rabbiting for these two farmers with guns, a spade, and probably ferrets. The postcard dates from about 1910.

3. Ulceby. The farm cart belongs to Ellis Ayre, who has obviously spent a lot of time polishing his cart and horse brasses ready for the local show sometime before the First World War.

INTRODUCTION

This book aims to provide readers with snapshots of Lincolnshire's past in an age when farmers were still largely dependent on manual labour and the horse. Most of the postcards featured here date from before 1920, when mechanisation was beginning to change farming practices, but when jobs on the farm were still very much labour-intensive. At the turn of the century 12% of male employment was still in farming, though this was a decreasing proportion, a trend that accelerated after the First World War. The advent of machinery was a key factor in this, though rural workers, on wages of as little as ten shillings a week in 1900, were continuing to be attracted by higher potential wages in factories.

Mechanical reapers became available by the end of the nineteenth century, though at first they were horse-drawn. Then came steam traction engines, fed on coal and water, which initially drew ploughs across fields by cable, but soon became adopted to many key jobs on the farm. The first petrol-driven tractor was introduced in 1902, and combine harvesters after 1918.

In Edwardian times, more than 60% of agricultural land in Lincolnshire was put down to crops, though Britain was already facing fierce competition from abroad; almost half of all food consumed was being imported, as well as three-quarters of grain used for making bread, despite politician Joseph Chamberlain's call for tariff reform and protection. Against this background, farmers had to adapt to survive, often concentrating on supplying their nearest urban markets or sending produce longer distances, helped by the improved facility for transporting goods by rail.

The illustrations in this book are all taken from picture postcards, which were hugely popular in the early years of this century as a means of sending photos of local scenes and events, or family pictures, to friends and relatives. Photographers like Simpson of Grantham or Blades of Horncastle published cards to record contemporary scenes in a way that newspapers were not yet able to do, and an efficient postal system allowed urgent messages to be sent in pre-telephone days.

Some of the cards are merely family portraits privately published in small numbers, while others indicate the power of the postcard as an advertising medium, with firms using them to promote their own agricultural products. Wherever known, the publisher of a particular card is acknowledged.

I hope you enjoy these glimpses of the past. I've used postcards to cover as many aspects of farming scenes and from as wide an area of the county as possible.

Eric Croft
May 1995

If any readers have postcards or photographs, or other information which might be useful for future publications, please contact me at 80 Yarborough Crescent, Lincoln (01522-539955).

Back cover (top): a group of female farm workers with pitchforks at Kirton End in 1908.

> **(bottom):** loading sheaves of mustard at a farm at Boston on a card posted from there in September 1913. The message reads: *"we are so busy with harvest – they have another three weeks of it yet. They had this took in the field when leading mustard. Robert is at the side of the wagon."*

4. Ulceby area. No machinery on show here in this c.1905 postcard view. The boy and girl are twisting straw to make bands to tie the corn into sheaves.

PEN OF EWES BRED BY J.B NELSON, BIGBY. 2 FIRSTS AND CHAMPION. XMAS 1906.

5. Bigby. The caption gives details of the sheep and their owner, with the prizes won at Brigg fair in 1906. The prize-winners are well overdue for clipping!

6. Brigg, where local photographer Grayson Clarke has recorded for one proud grower a root of 'Defiance' potatoes picked in August (about 1906).

7. Owston Ferry. A card from the early 1920s showing a manual baling apparatus and cutting knife. Note the way the stack is cut in 'steps'.

8. Scotter. A farmyard threshing scene. Many hands were needed despite mechanisation.

9. A tractor and binder at **Scotter,** before the days of the combine harvesters, which began to be used after the First World War. The village, near Kirton-in-Lindsey, had a population of just over a thousand at the start of the century.

10. Fine specimen of a prize bull at **Kirton Lindsey,** featured on a card posted there in June 1906. The sender has written *"here's a card for your album".*

11. Nettleton, near Caistor, and another anonymously-published card of a threshing scene about 1910. Groups of workers were frequently photographed onto postcards which could be sent to friends and relatives.

12. A farmyard scene at **Blyton,** north of Gainsborough, in 1912.

13. A photograph of an early International tractor at **Willoughton** c.1920. No danger of skidding with tractor wheels like these, almost ploughs in themselves. The wheels were also wide-based to make it less likely that the vehicle would become bogged down.

14. Traction engine at **Claxby** in 1911. Three miles north of Market Rasen, this village had a population of under 300 at the time. The introduction of steam-driven engines on the farm was to revolutionise the labour market.

15. A field of giant white clover at **Heapham,** sowed for seed on the farms of Messrs. Hird and Sons.

16. Haymaking at **North Willingham.** The cart is clearly owned by Tom Willey, and it looks as though the whole family have come out for this photograph!

HORSE FAIR 'SALTFLEET 580

17. Saltfleet Horse Fair – obviously a big occasion, with horses being auctioned. It must have been the local farmers' excuse for a day off. Card published by J.S. Bullen of Grimsby, but not dated.

18. Ingham. A postcard of Tom Bristow who worked for over 60 years on the same farm at Ingham. This card dates from the early 1930s.

19. Cammeringham farmstead, with the people in the photograph in typical Edwardian dress. Pigs, cattle and dogs mingle contentedly. In 1904, this village had a population of 138.

20. These pigs at a farm at **Scampton,** near Lincoln, pictured about 1923, could well be the now extinct Lincolnshire curly coats.

21. A ploughing scene at **Broxholme** in the early 1920s, with a two-in-hand. Six miles north-west of Lincoln, this village had a population of just over a hundred at the turn of the century.

22. One of a number of machines in a ploughing exhibition at **North Carlton** in the 1920s. Both the machine and the driver's hat carry a numbered label.

23. Welton. A threshing scene at a farm on Welton Cliff c.1910. The portable steam engine was probably manufactured by Ruston of Lincoln.

24. Saxilby. Mrs Marrison and Mrs Ferris are feeding their free range poultry in a field which was also used as the local football pitch. The card was published about 1912.

25. A farm near **Wragby** during the First World War, with a group of workers in military uniform baling hay commandeered by the War Office. Four of the group are young women, presumably land army girls.

26. Farmer Tom Marrison ploughing at **Nettleham** about 1908. In Edwardian days, this was a long and tiring job. The ploughman had to control a team of horses to pull a single furrow plough, and took pride in the furrow being straight!

27. Postcard showing carrots being harvested, topped and bagged on a farm at **Eagle** in the late 1920s.

Upwards of 100,000 of CLAYTON & SHUTTLEWORTH'S
Engines and Thrashing Machines have been
made and sold.

28. An advertising postcard for the Lincoln firm of Clayton & Shuttleworth's portable engine. This is one of several cards published by the firm of Ruddock in Lincoln, and dates from 1907.

The Cattle Market, Lincoln.

29. Lincoln Cattle Market on Monks Road, a thriving sc⋯
posted at Torksey in November 1910; like most cards ⋯
farming products appear on hoardings above their office⋯

far from the city centre. Postcard published by Boots, and
cattle market, it features sheep in the pens. Adverts for
centre of the picture.

30. A farmer's day out to **Horncastle** Horse Fair in 1915 on an attractively animated card published by A. Blades of Horncastle. According to a 1900 edition of Kelly's local directory, this event was held in August and considered to be *"the greatest horse fair in the kingdom"*.

31. An engine manufactured by the firm of Allchin seen on a farm at **Mablethorpe** in the late 1920s.

32. Hameringham. A card by Blades of Horncastle showing a rather macabre scene of some of 30 sheep killed by lightning in July of one year c.1912.

33. Bassingham, and a wonderfully improvised scene in 1912. Apparently the traction engine on Mr. Roberts' farm had broken down, so the drive lift for the elevator is being run off the rear hub of the car. The vehicle is being held in place by means of a chain and iron bar!

34. A typical threshing scene on a card posted at **Martin** in May 1904. The portable engine was manufactured by Ruston Proctor & Co. of Lincoln.

35. A lovely summer scene in the early 1920s at **Nocton,** a small village eight miles south-east of Lincoln. Hay is being transported on these two trailers.

36. Thorpe-on-the-Hill, six miles south-west of Lincoln, with farmer Mr. Holman harrowing with a team of three horses. The card was posted from the village in October 1921.

37. Burgh-le-Marsh, with a corn binder in action. The nearby market town in East Lincolnshire had a population of 974 in 1901.

38. A load of sacks, possibly corn, being transported by a four-horse team on a farm at **Burgh-le-Marsh.**

39. Stickney. A cultivator with a Fowler single-cylinder ploughing engine on a farm at Stickney in the 1920s. The cultivator was hauled across the fields between a pair of engines by means of a wire rope on a drum mechanism under each engine. On reaching the engines, the cultivator was reversed, each engine moved on a few feet, and the cultivator would be hauled back to the other side.

40. Fulbeck, where a local farmer has been testing fertilisers on his mangel crop. The point of the photograph is to show that 'Kainit' (advertised on the reverse) produced a much greater yield when added to the natural fertilisers of dung, bones and slag.

41. Long Bennington. A local farmer is waiting to unload his corn at the village's water mill. The postcard was published by Simpson & Son of Grantham, and posted at Long Bennington in August 1912. This building is now in a very dilapidated state.

42. A busy day at **Sleaford** cattle market pictured on a postcard by Chilton of that town about 1910. The market closed in November 1984 and is now a housing estate. Market days provided a much-needed social occasion for local farmers.

43. Roxholm, three miles north of Sleaford, had a population of just 118 in 1904. This card shows a busy threshing scene on the farm of Cole Bros., the major local landowners. The threshing machine was manufactured by Ransome, Sims & Jeffries.

44. North Kyme. This rather gruesome photograph is typical of what was once a common sight throughout the county. Every farmer and most farm workers would kill a pig during the winter months. No butchers involved, no health regulations, and no freezers!. The postcard was published about 1920.

45. Benington. The card features Disbrowe's Nurseries at the village near Boston, and the gentleman in the picture is probably Mr. Disbrowe himself, obviously proud of his crop of Northern Stars potatoes. Postcard sent from Boston in January 1905.

46. This photograph was taken at **Leverton** during the First World War, and the ladies outnumber the men! Only the army could think of weighing the bales – note the weighing machine and weights on the left. The traction engine is a Fowler, and the baler was manufactured by Rustons.

47. Boston cattle market in 1904 on a card published by E.W. Peakome. As with the Lincoln and Sleaford cards *(see illus. 29 and 42),* the pens are full of sheep, with no cattle in sight!

48. Another baling scene, this time at **Welton,** near Lincoln, during World War One. The William Foster engine was owned by Thomas Storin of Welton, but the card publisher was Simpson of Grantham. The army seem to have commandeered the traction engine for the war effort.

49. No fewer than eight men are shearing sheep here on a card from the **Grantham** area about 1912. Lincolnshire boasted about 450 sheep per square mile on its agricultural land, one of the highest densities in the country.

50. A shepherd with his dog and flock at **Gedney.** He may possibly have been the sender of this card in March 1908 – J.R. Needham, of Red House Farm, Gedney Marsh.

51. Threshing scene at **Birthorpe** about 1910 on the farm of J. Tomlinson. The photographic card clearly emphasises the labour-intensive nature of all farming tasks, even after the introduction of traction engines.

52. Welby, and a sad scene after a fire which has done fairly intensive damage to what appears to be a threshing machine. The straw seems relatively untouched!

53. Spalding. A commercially-published card by the Spalding Free Press in their 'Flower Culture' series. Captioned 'gathering pyrethrums', the card was posted at Spalding in June 1914.